Charlie Brown!

Selected Cartoons from
*GOOD GRIEF,
MORE PEANUTS!*
VOL. 1

by Charles M. Schulz

A FAWCETT CREST BOOK

Fawcett Publications, Inc., Greenwich, Conn.
Member of American Book Publishers Council, Inc.

GOOD GRIEF, CHARLIE BROWN!

This book, prepared especially for Fawcett Publications, Inc.,
comprises the first half of GOOD GRIEF, MORE PEANUTS!,
and is reprinted by arrangement with Holt, Rinehart
and Winston, Inc.

Fifteenth Fawcett Crest printing, March 1968

Published by Fawcett World Library,
67 West 44th Street, New York, New York 10036
Printed in the United States of America

Good Grief, Charlie Brown!

KRINKLE

THAT COST MY DAD TWELVE DOLLARS!

SCHULZ